The Voice of the Martyrs

PO Box 443,
Bartlesville, OK 74005

The Story of St. Patrick

MORE THAN SHAMROCKS AND LEPRECHAUNS

Written by The Voice of the Martyrs
with Cheryl Odden
Illustrated by R.F. Palavicini
and Castle Animation

The Voice of the Martyrs is a Christian nonprofit organization
dedicated to helping those who are persecuted for their
Christian witness in communist, Islamic and other nations
hostile to Christ. In 1967, after being ransomed from
communist Romania, Richard and Sabina Wurmbrand came
to the U.S. and began their ministry to the persecuted
church. Their vision was global, and a network of offices
was birthed to raise awareness of and take relief to those
suffering for their Christian witness.

For a free, monthly newsletter and ways you can help
today's persecuted church, contact:

The Voice of the Martyrs
PO Box 443
Bartlesville, OK 74005
(800) 747-0085
E-mail: thevoice@vom-usa.org
Web site: www.persecution.com

For the children who have lost one or both parents because of their Christian witness in nations hostile to Jesus. May you see God as your Father, who will always be there to provide for you and comfort you!

For every child who dares to respond to God's voice and boldly share Jesus with friends and family members. May God be glorified in your words and actions, drawing many into a relationship with Him!

Many celebrate Saint Patrick's Day on March 17th and hang pictures of shamrocks and mythical creatures called leprechauns. But who was Saint Patrick, and why do we celebrate his life on this day?

Patrick lived a full life, but not without his share of suffering and adventure. He was born in Britain, in the fourth century A.D., during a time of great uncertainty for the Roman Empire. The Roman legions that once protected civilized Britain from barbaric invaders were called away to defend themselves in other regions of the Roman Empire. Therefore, Britain was left vulnerable to attacks.

Just before Patrick turned 16 years of age, he and his family were at their holiday villa by the sea, located outside the town of Bannaventa Berniae when Irish pirates attacked it just before dawn. (Some say the villa was attacked during the day while Patrick played on the beach.) Although Patrick's family escaped, Patrick and many of the family's workers did not; and soon they were en route to Ireland, where Patrick was sold as a slave to Miliuc of Slemich, a Druid tribal chieftain.

Patrick was given the task of a herdsman. Though raised in a Christian home (his father, Calpornius, was a civil magistrate and tax collector, as well as a church deacon), Patrick never made a decision to follow Christ until he was kidnapped and made a slave. In his autobiography called *Confessions,* Patrick wrote: "…'the Lord opened my senses to my unbelief,' so that though late in the day, I might remember my many sins; and accordingly 'I might turn to the Lord my God with all my heart.'" He also wrote about how his faith in God grew as he prayed to Him while he shepherded the flocks: "But after I had come to Ireland, it was then that I was made to shepherd the flocks day after day, and, as I did so, I would pray all the time, right through the day. More and more the love of God and fear of him grew strong within me, and as my faith grew, so the Spirit became more and more active…. In snow, in frost, in rain, I would hardly notice any discomfort, and I was never slack but always full of energy. It is clear to me now, that this was due to…the Spirit within me."

But Patrick's devotion to God did not go unnoticed. He soon earned the nickname "Holy Boy" among his fellow slaves.

One night Patrick had a dream, and in it he heard a voice saying to him, "You are right to fast, soon you will be returning to your own country." In another dream he received a response to the first dream, being told, "Come and see where your ship is waiting for you." At the age of 22, Patrick escaped and traveled 200 miles to the coast of Ireland. Of his long journey across Ireland, he wrote: "I turned on my heel and ran away, leaving behind the man to whom I had been bound for six years. Yet I came away from him in the power of God, for it was he who was guiding my every step for the best. And so I felt not the least anxiety until I reached the ship."

When Patrick approached one of the men on the ship that was on the coast, he asked to board. The seaman scowled at him, so Patrick began to leave when the man called back to him, saying the other men wanted him on board as a passenger. Patrick wrote, "In spite of this, I still hoped that they might come to have faith in Jesus Christ."

The journey by boat was long, including a stop on land where they journeyed for 28 days. After having run out of food, the captain turned to Patrick and challenged him to ask his God for food. Glad to oblige, Patrick responded: "Turn trustingly to the Lord who is my God and put your faith in him with all your heart, because nothing is impossible to him. On this day, he will send us food sufficient for our journey, because for him there is abundance everywhere." According to Patrick's autobiography, when the men turned around, a herd of pigs was standing before them. They feasted for days and gave thanks to God.

Two years later Patrick finally made it to his beloved Britain and into the arms of his mother and father who pled with him never to leave them again. Patrick began to settle back into his life in Britain and studied to become a priest and bishop. But one night Patrick had a dream of a man who seemed to come from Ireland and was carrying a letter with the words "The Voice of the Irish." As Patrick began to read the words, he seemed to hear the voice of the same men he worked with as if they were shouting, "Holy broth of a boy, we beg you, come back and walk once more among us."

But Patrick's plans to return to Ireland—the land of his captivity—were fiercely opposed by both his parents and the church leaders who, by the way, did not think the Druids were worth saving. His family shuddered at the thought of him returning to barbaric Ireland with the gospel, as the Druids were known to weave criminals and runaway slaves into giant wicker baskets and suspend them over a fire. Of this opposition Patrick later wrote: "So at last I came here to the Irish gentiles to preach the gospel. And now I had to endure insults from unbelievers, to 'hear criticism of my journeys,' and suffer many persecutions 'even to the point of chains.'… And should I prove worthy, I am ready and willing to give up my own life, without hesitation for his name…. There was always someone talking behind my back and whispering, 'Why does he want to put himself in such danger among his enemies who do not know God?'" Patrick had to sell his title of nobility in order to become the "slave of Christ serving the barbaric nation."

While Patrick was in Ireland, he shared the gospel with his former slave owner, Miliuc the Druid. But instead of turning his back on his pagan gods, Miliuc locked himself in his house and set it on fire while Patrick stood outside the house and pled with him to turn to Christ. It is said Miliuc drowned out Patrick's pleadings by crying out to his false gods.

But Miliuc's refusal to hear the gospel was just the beginning of Patrick's challenges with the Druids as he spread the gospel across Ireland and taught the people how to read and write. One story that some believe is legend mentions Patrick challenging the Druid wizards in 433 A.D., on the vernal equinox, which occurred on Easter Sunday that year. Patrick challenged the wizards' power of control by starting a bonfire, which was central to the Druids' ritual, on a hillside opposite of the barbaric idol-worshippers. Patrick was dragged before the Druid council where he had the opportunity to share about Jesus, the light of the world. Some Druids believed, and others tried to kill him.

Patrick continued his journey across Ireland. He preached at racetracks and other places of worldly indulgences, seeing many come to Christ. However, this was not unmet with opposition. The Druids often tried to poison him. One time a barbarian warrior speared Patrick's chariot driver to death in an attempt to kill Patrick. He was often ambushed at his evangelistic events, and it is noted that he was enslaved again for a short time. He had to purchase safe passage through a hostile warlord's land in order to continue on his journey. Another time Patrick and his companions were taken as prisoners and were going to be killed, but they were later released. In *Confessions*, Patrick wrote, "As every day arrives, I expect either sudden death or deception or being taken back as a slave or some such other misfortune. But I fear none of these, since I look to the promise of heaven and have flung myself into the hands of the all-powerful God, who rules as Lord everywhere."

Patrick journeyed throughout Ireland, sharing Christ until his death on March 17th, around the year 461 A.D. Later Irish mythological creatures known as leprechauns would creep into the holiday celebrations, as well as the symbol of the shamrock, believed to have been used by Patrick to illustrate the Trinity as he preached and taught. Some legends have circulated stating Patrick drove all the snakes out of Ireland. Since there are no snakes in Ireland and snakes symbolize the devil and evil, many believe the "snakes" were a metaphor representing his work of driving the idol-worshipping Druid cult out of the country.

Enslavement, torture, imprisonment and death for one's faith in Christ were not confined to Patrick's lifetime. Today Christians in communist nations like China, Vietnam and Cuba are imprisoned if caught sharing the gospel with fellow countrymen. In Sudan, a Christian boy named Demare was kidnapped by militant Muslims and sold as a slave. And in Vietnam, when members of some tribal groups have come to Christ, they destroy the altars used to pray to their dead ancestors. When fellow villagers and even members of the government hear about this, these new believers in Christ are harassed and some even imprisoned for turning away from their empty religions of idol and ancestor worship.

We may never be enslaved, imprisoned or beaten because of our faith in Christ, but many may make fun of us for believing in Jesus' promise of heaven and placing our faith in a God they do not see with their eyes and cannot touch with their hands. I pray this version of Patrick's courageous life will inspire you to stand firm in Christ and stand strong for Him as you tell others about the greatest gift we can ever be given—salvation through Jesus!

Quoted material featured in the "Note from the Author" from *The Confession of Saint Patrick* by John O'Donohue (trans) (New York, NY: Image Books, a division of Bantam Doubleday Dell Publishing Group, Inc., 1998).

For a complete listing of resources consulted in the writing of the story and the "Note from the Author," see the Bibliography on page 42.

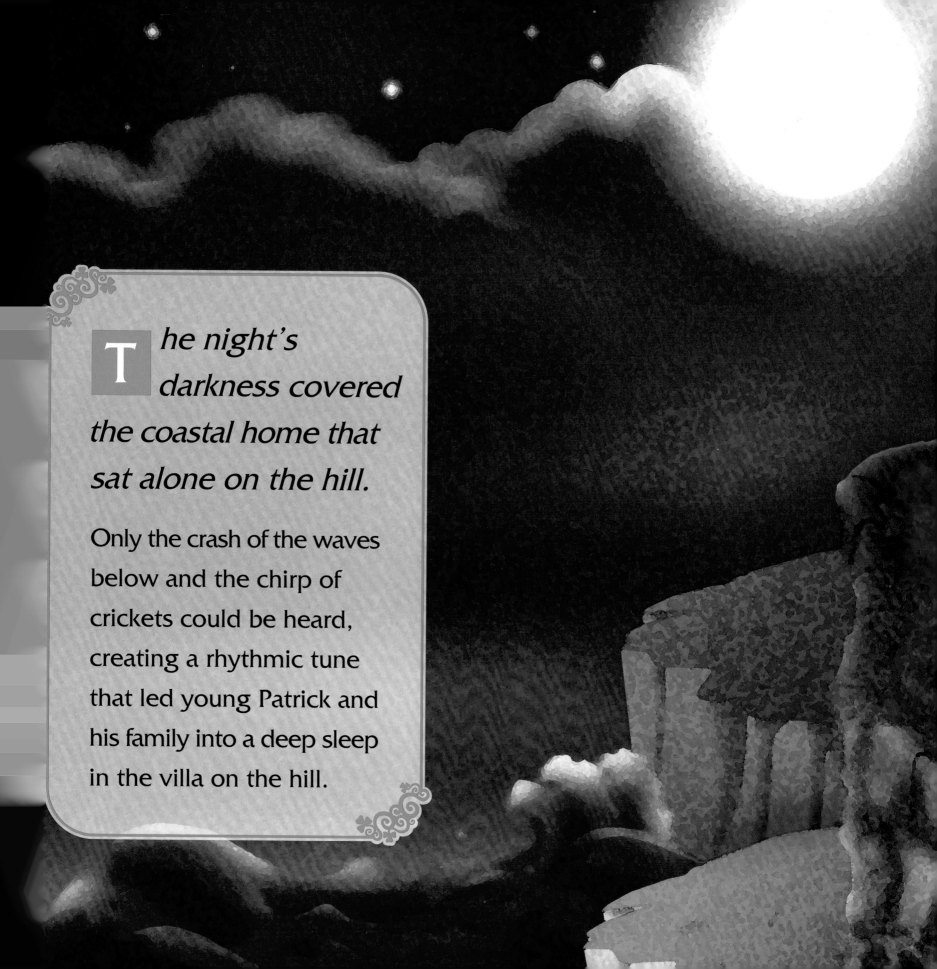

T he night's darkness covered the coastal home that sat alone on the hill.

Only the crash of the waves below and the chirp of crickets could be heard, creating a rhythmic tune that led young Patrick and his family into a deep sleep in the villa on the hill.

But as the wind whispered and the waves walloped the sandy beach below, pirates from a land across the sea crept closer and closer in their large wicker boats.

The oarsmen quietly pulled the large paddles of the sea vessels until they safely reached the shore. The pirates jumped out of the boats, their boots hitting the grains of sand, and without making a sound, the captain pointed to the villa on the hill.

It didn't take the pirates long to surround the coastal home covered in darkness. With the sound of a shout, the pirate's captain cried, "Attack!" and his men burst into the villa, with orders to capture everyone in sight.

Young Patrick thought he was dreaming when he heard his father's footsteps in the hallway outside his bedroom door.

"Wake up! Wake up! Pirates are invading our villa!" But before Patrick could leap to his feet, a pirate grabbed him by the arm. "You're coming with me!" he gruffly growled and hauled his prisoner away to the wicker boats waiting on the sand of the shore below.

When they reached the shore, Patrick was thrown into the bottom of one of the boats with several other prisoners.

Patrick began to wonder as he wept. *"Where is my family? Did they escape?"* Soon Patrick fell asleep to the sound of the oarsmen chanting their commands as the sea vessel departed, leaving behind his family and the villa on the hill.

9

The boat sailed until it reached the strange shoreline.

One of the pirates came stomping down into the bowels of the boat and barked to the prisoners, "On your feet!" Patrick followed his fellow captives onto the deck of the boat and into the blinding daylight. Never had he seen so many shades of green as he marveled at the majestic mounds of land looming before him.

P atrick and the other prisoners formed a line and looked into the strange faces standing before them.

"What will you give me for this boy?" cried the captain as he pointed at Patrick, who stood shaking in fear. "I'll pay you double for him!" bellowed a burly man with a deep, husky voice. "I need a young man like him to herd my sheep." With that Patrick was taken away by the burly man who was now his master. *"I'm a slave!"* panicked Patrick silently in his thoughts, and he began to lose hope he would ever see his family again.

Patrick was taken to his master's home where he was given a place to sleep and his orders to tend the sheep.

His master was very harsh. His words had a roughness to them that Patrick was not used to. But every morning, he would dutifully awaken and lead the sheep out into the pastures.

14

One day as Patrick tended sheep in the lush, green fields, he began to think of his father.

Patrick never paid much attention to his father's reading of Scriptures or stories of Jesus. But now that he was all alone tending sheep on the hillside of the strange, green land, it was just him and God. He missed his family so much his heart began to ache. So he fell on his knees and prayed: "Dear God, I need You! I have lost my family, my father. Be a Father to me as I serve here in this strange land as a slave." As soon as Patrick finished praying, his heart was filled with a peace he had never experienced until that time.

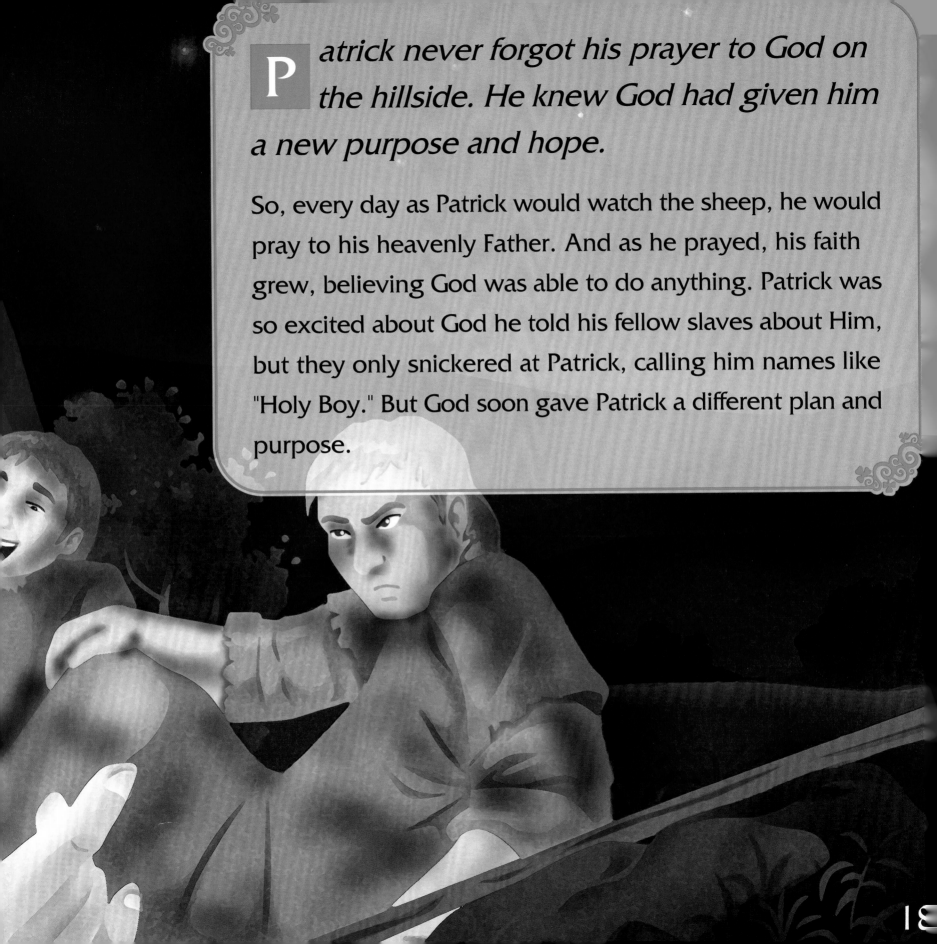

Patrick never forgot his prayer to God on the hillside. He knew God had given him a new purpose and hope.

So, every day as Patrick would watch the sheep, he would pray to his heavenly Father. And as he prayed, his faith grew, believing God was able to do anything. Patrick was so excited about God he told his fellow slaves about Him, but they only snickered at Patrick, calling him names like "Holy Boy." But God soon gave Patrick a different plan and purpose.

One night as Patrick slept, he had a dream. "Soon you will be returning home!" proclaimed the mysterious messenger.

Patrick sat up, a rush of hope filled his heart. *"Could I be going home?"* he wondered and laid his head back down on the hard earth until he was awakened by yet another dream. "Come and see where your ship is waiting for you!" cried the mysterious messenger. Patrick awoke, knowing it was time for him to escape from his master and return to his family. So Patrick tip-toed through the sleeping slaves with a knapsack on his back and new hope in his heart.

Patrick traveled on foot for many days before he reached the shores of the strange, green land.

When he saw a single boat waiting to set sail, he remembered the mysterious messenger in his dream. He walked up to the boat and hollered at one of the scruffy seamen, "May I join you on your voyage?" The man wrinkled his forehead and scowled, "And why should we take you with us? You're just another mouth to feed!" As Patrick's hope began to fade, he heard the scruffy seaman shout, "Wait! The other men want you to come with us! Must be your lucky day!" Patrick boarded the boat, which soon departed the shores of the strange, green land and made its way across the waters.

*T*hree days after the ship set sail, the crew brought the vessel to another strange land.

For many days they explored until they had finally run out of food and were weak with hunger. The captain looked at Patrick and mocked, "If you say your God is so great, then why don't you ask Him for food?" Patrick took up the captain's challenge and said, "Trust in God with all your heart. Nothing is impossible for Him!" Suddenly the men turned around, and there before them was a herd of pigs! The men feasted for days and gave thanks to God until it was time to board the ship and set sail to get ever closer to Patrick's homeland.

Soon the ship reached the shores of Patrick's homeland. Patrick darted off the boat and ran to his home and into the arms of his mother and father.

"We have been so worried about you, Patrick! We didn't know if you had survived the pirates' invasion of our villa on the hill! Please don't ever leave us again!" they pled.

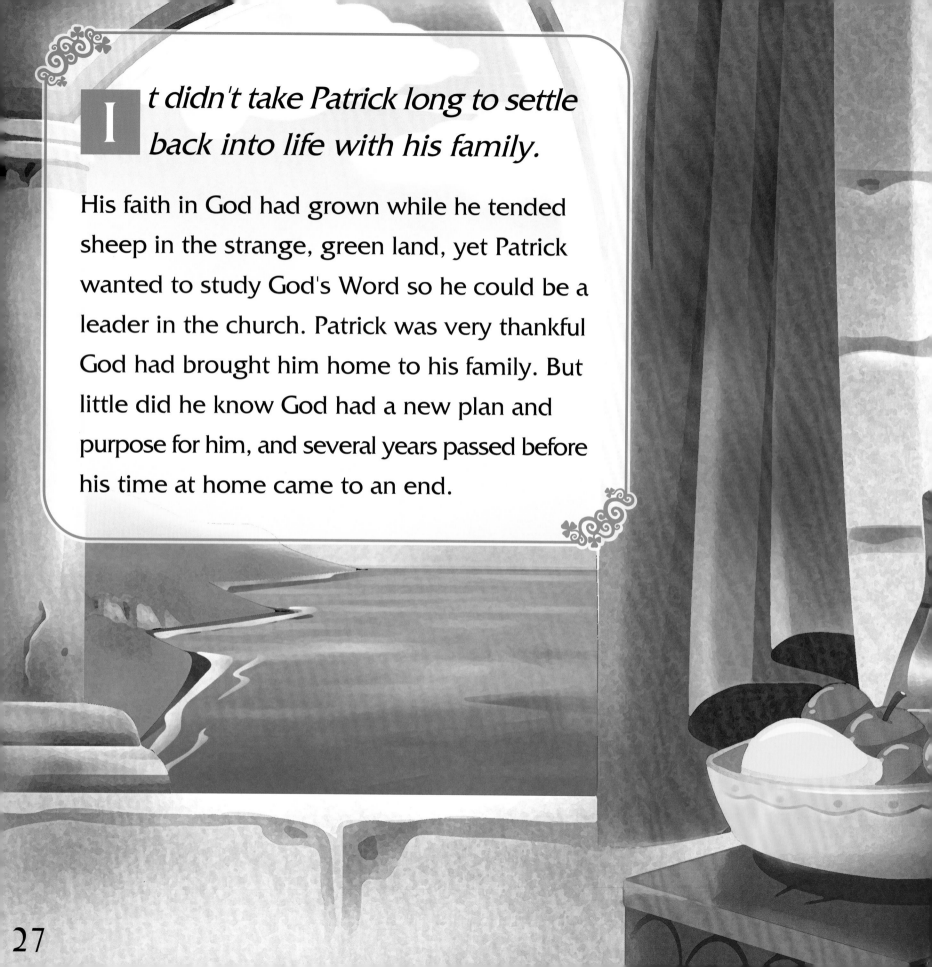

It didn't take Patrick long to settle back into life with his family.

His faith in God had grown while he tended sheep in the strange, green land, yet Patrick wanted to study God's Word so he could be a leader in the church. Patrick was very thankful God had brought him home to his family. But little did he know God had a new plan and purpose for him, and several years passed before his time at home came to an end.

One night as Patrick slept soundly, he had another dream. This time in his dream, a man from the strange, green land where he served as a slave came to him and handed him a letter.

The letter reminded Patrick of those he left behind as if they were saying, "Holy Boy, we beg you. Come back! Come back and walk with us once more!" Patrick awoke the next morning, convinced of what he must do: He must return to the strange, green land and tell them about the God who saved him as he served as a slave.

But Patrick's family and the church leaders did not want him to return to the strange, green land.

"How could you leave us again? Don't you know what they do to slaves who run away from their masters?" his family cried. "The people in the strange, green land are brutal barbarians and have no interest in God. They even made you a slave," the church leaders insisted. But Patrick knew he needed to obey God and return with His message of salvation through Jesus—the very message that saved him as a slave on the hillside as he herded sheep. So Patrick said goodbye to his family and departed for the strange, green land.

When Patrick reached the strange, green land, he traveled the countryside, telling people about Jesus and teaching them how to read and write.

He was overjoyed how the people who had known and worshipped nothing but idols were turning to God. But there were many who were furious with Patrick. They didn't like it that he was teaching the people how to read and write and leading people away from their idols. They were so angry they tried to poison Patrick. Another tried to kill him, but he escaped and continued traveling the countryside.

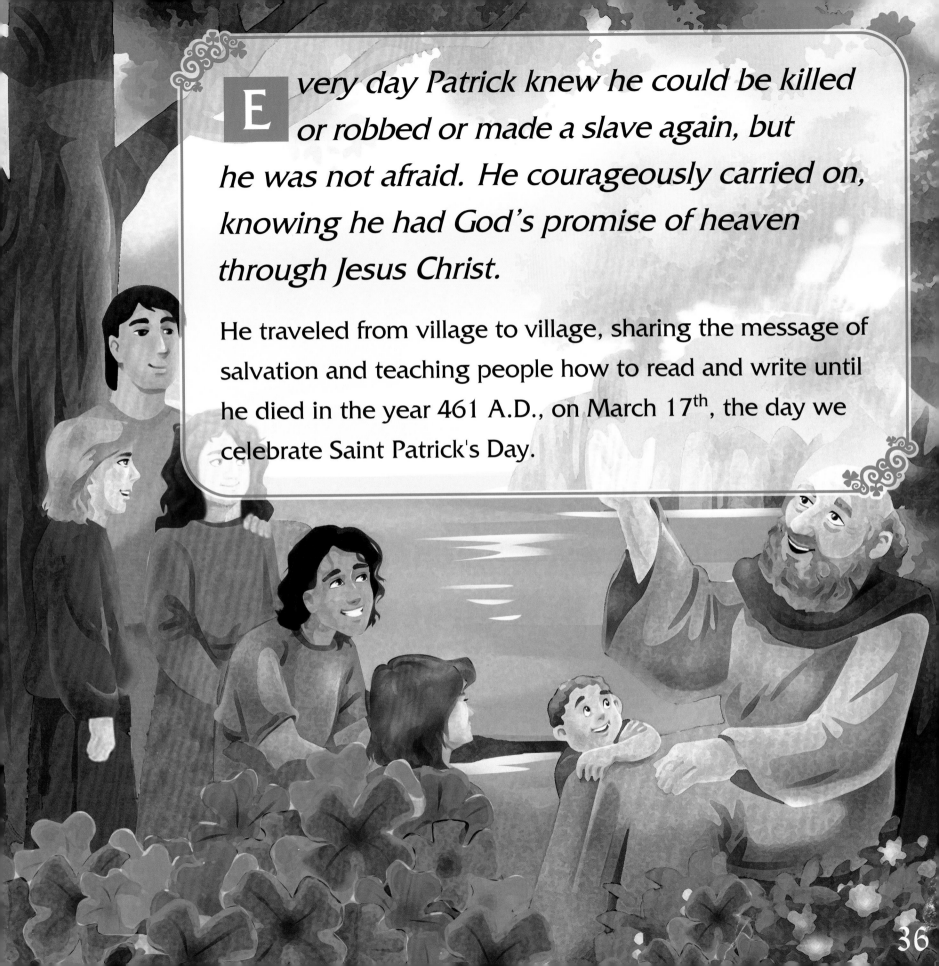

Every day Patrick knew he could be killed or robbed or made a slave again, but he was not afraid. He courageously carried on, knowing he had God's promise of heaven through Jesus Christ.

He traveled from village to village, sharing the message of salvation and teaching people how to read and write until he died in the year 461 A.D., on March 17th, the day we celebrate Saint Patrick's Day.

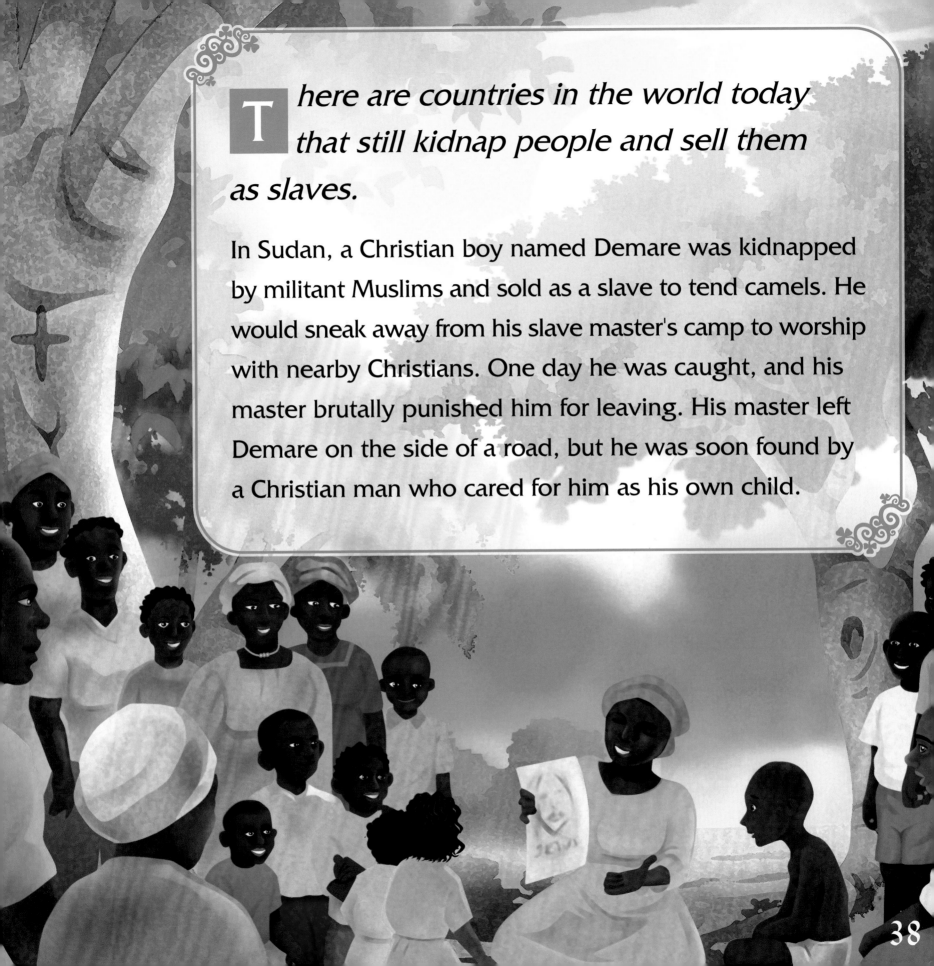

There are countries in the world today that still kidnap people and sell them as slaves.

In Sudan, a Christian boy named Demare was kidnapped by militant Muslims and sold as a slave to tend camels. He would sneak away from his slave master's camp to worship with nearby Christians. One day he was caught, and his master brutally punished him for leaving. His master left Demare on the side of a road, but he was soon found by a Christian man who cared for him as his own child.

We may never be kidnapped by people of a strange land and forced to tend sheep or camels, but like Patrick, our friends may laugh at us for believing in a God we cannot see with our eyes.

As God's children, we have the same message as Patrick and Demare: the "promise of heaven"! It's a promise for everyone who chooses to believe in Jesus Christ.

For Further Reflection

"And you will be hated by all for My name's sake.
But he who endures to the end will be saved."
The words of Jesus as recorded in Matthew 10:22

In the strange, green land that we know as Ireland, how was Patrick
treated by the people he tried to reach for Christ?
How did Patrick respond when he was treated that way?
How do your friends treat you when you tell them about Jesus?
The word "endure" means "under misfortunes and trials to hold fast to
one's faith in Christ" and "to bear bravely and calmly." What did Patrick
endure as he shared the gospel in Ireland?

Prayer
Dear Jesus, I have friends who do not know You. I ask for boldness
and graciousness to tell them about the promise of heaven You
have offered to each of us who chooses to receive it. If they make fun
of me for following a God they cannot see or for believing in a promise
they do not understand, help me stay close to You, and not be ashamed
of You.
Amen.

[1] From the Greek word *hupomeno*.